# A Day in the Life of ™

# Flippidy Frog

by

Betty Preston

SCHOLASTIC INC.

New York   Toronto   London   Auckland   Sydney
Mexico City   New Delhi   Hong Kong   Buenos Aires

## Photo Credits

Patti Bartlett—pp. 17, 18-19
James Beveridge/Visuals Unlimited—p. 16
FPG International—Cover, p. 14
Robert and Linda Mitchell—pp. 4, 5, 7, 24
Zig Leszczynski—pp. 3, 6, 8-9, 10, 11, 12, 13, 15, 20-21, 21, 22, 23

ISBN 0-439-46095-6

12 11 10 9 8 7 6 5 4 3 2 1          3 4 5 6 7 8/ 0

Printed in the U.S.A.          23

First Scholastic printing, March 2003

Flippidy is a red-eyed tree frog.

She was born in Panama, a country in Central America.

3

Flippidy lives in the rain forest. She spends her day in the trees and . . .

. . . on flowers.

Red-eyed tree frogs sleep during the day. When Flippidy wakes up, it is nighttime for you!

Flippidy is hungry.
She climbs onto a rock
to look for her favorite
snacks: flies, moths,
and grasshoppers.

7

After eating, Flippidy joins her cousins
on a tree branch. Hello, tree frogs!

It is getting crowded on
Flippidy's branch.

She springs with her strong legs to a nearby leaf.

Flippidy
goes exploring.
She finds her
friend, Jasper.
He is much
smaller than
she is.

Boy tree frogs are always much smaller than girl tree frogs.

The yellow-orange pads on a tree frog's feet are sticky. They help Flippidy cling to leaves and branches.

Jasper sees a nice spot for a snooze. He tucks in all his bright colors, so other animals can't see him while he is asleep.

Under Jasper's leaf, Flippidy sees tree frog eggs! You can see tiny tadpoles swimming around in some of them.

When the tadpoles are big enough, they will break out of their eggs and fall into a pond. At first, tadpoles look like fish.

Then they grow legs!
As the tadpoles grow, they
will look more and more
like Flippidy.

Flippidy hangs out on a branch, looking around. If another animal comes by, Flippidy can turn her head suddenly and open her eyes wide. Those bright red eyes will scare the other animal and give Flippidy a chance to hop away.

Flippidy hears lots of chirping, so she hops down to see what it is.

It is her cousins! When tree frogs get together, they make lots of chirping and rattling sounds. It is just like a tree frog chorus!

Flippidy sees the sun coming up. Since tree frogs sleep during the day, Flippidy finds a nice, comfy spot.

23

Good night, Flippidy. Sweet dreams!